starsailo

love is here

guitar tablature vocal

www. starsailor .net

production anna joyce
folio design dominic brookman
music arranged by artemis music ltd
cover photography by image state
sleeve design by adjective noun

published 2001

© international music publications ltd
griffin house 161 hammersmith road london w6 8bs england

tie up my hands

wipe the make-up from your face
tie your hair and gently fall from grace
until i come again
take the disaffected life
men who ran the company ran your life
you could have been his wife

i wanna love you but my hands are tied
i wanna stay here but i've been denied
lets watch the clock until the morning sun does rise

wipe the sweat from off your brow
all that you believe is here and now
you could have had more doubt

wipe the shadow from your eyes
rest your daughter while your mother cries
you could have let him fly

i wanna hold you but my hands are tied
i wanna stay here but i've been denied
i wanna lie here 'til we've killed this bitter doubt

i wanna hold you but my hands are tied
i wanna stay here but i've been denied
lets watch the clock until the morning sun does rise

i wanna hold you but my hands are tied
i wanna sleep here but i've been denied
i wanna stay here 'til we've killed this bitter doubt

i wanna hold you but my hands are tied
i wanna sleep here but i've been denied
lets watch the clock until the morning sun comes out

poor misguided fool

as soon as you sound like him
give me a call
when you're so sensitive
its a long way to fall

whenever you need a home
i will be there
whenever you're all alone
and nobody cares

you're just a poor misguided fool
who thinks they know what i should do
a line for me and a line for you
i lose my right to a point of view

whenever you reach for me
i'll be your guide
whenever you need someone
to keep it inside

whenever you need a home
i will be there
whenever you're all alone
and nobody cares

you're just a poor misguided fool
who thinks they know what i should do
a line for me and a line for you
i lose my right to a point of view

i'll be your guide in the morning
you cover up bullet holes

as soon as you sound like him
give me a call
when you're so sensitive
its a long way to fall

you're just a poor misguided fool
who thinks they know what i should do
a line for me and a line for you
i lose my right to a point of view

alcoholic

don't you know you've got your daddy's eyes
and your daddy was an alcoholic
but your mother kept it all inside
threw it all away

i was looking for another you
and i found another one
i was looking for another you
when i looked round you were gone

stay by my side
and the pipe dream is yours now
stay by my side
and the singer won't get in our way

don't you know you've got your daddy's eyes
and your daddy was an alcoholic
but your mother kept it all inside
threw it all away

i was looking for another you
and i found another one
i was looking for another you
when i looked round you were gone

stay by my side
and the pipe dream is yours now
stay by my side
and the cynics won't get in our way

don't you know you've got your daddy's eyes
and your daddy was an alcoholic
but your mother kept it all inside
threw it all away
i was looking for another chance
to see your blue eyed problem

lullaby

get back on your feet again
so insincere
quiet american
i held you so dear

get back on your feet again
i'm so into you
we met in a cinema
you fell from my view

lullaby
stop twisting my words tonight
if you get high on life
don't leave me behind

get back on your feet again
nothing to say
some of your weaker friends
get in my away

get back on your feet again
you always seem down
some of your weaker friends
don't want you around

lullaby
stop twisting my words tonight
if you get high on life
don't leave me behind

lullaby
you live in my ruined mind
make light of all my fears
and lead me from here

get back on your feet again
so insincere
quiet american
i held you so dear

get back on your feet again
nothing to say
we met in a cinema
you got in my way

lullaby
stop twisting my words tonight
if you get high on life
don't leave me behind

lullaby
you live in my ruined mind
make light of all my fears
and lead me from here

way to fall

son
you've got a way to fall
they'll tell you where to go
but they won't know

son
you'd better take it all
they'll tell you what they know
but they won't show

oh
i've got something in my throat
i need to be alone
while i suffer

son
you've got a way to kill
they're picking on you still
but they don't know

son
you'd better wait to shine
they'll tell you what is yours
but they'll take mine

oh
i've got something in my throat
i need to be alone
while i suffer

oh
there's a hole inside my boat
and i need stay afloat
for the summer
long

oh
i've got something in my throat
i need to be alone
while i suffer

oh
there's a hole inside my boat
and i need stay afloat
for the summer

son
you've got to wait to fall
they'll tell you where to go
but they won't know

fever

there's a fever
on the freeway
in the morning
in the morning
and the lover
smiling for me
without warning
without warning

there's an outlaw
on the highway
and she's falling
and she's falling

man i must have been blind
to carry a torch
for most of my life
these days i'm hanging around
you're out of my heart
and out of my town

there's a fever
on the freeway
in the morning
in the morning
and the lover
smiling for me
while she's falling
while she's falling

man i must have been blind
to carry a torch
for most of my life
these days i'm hanging around
you're out of my heart
and out of my town

there's a fever
on the freeway
in the morning
in the morning
and the lover
smiling for me
without warning
without warning

man i must have been blind
to carry a torch
for most of my life
these days i'm hanging around
you're out of my heart
and out of my town

she just wept

she just wept
like i could not ignore
how can i act
when my heart's on the floor?
she just wept
'til her eyes became sore
i knew who she was
but i don't anymore

she just cried
to the ruins of time
that kept us apart
we were doing just fine
she just wept
she was put to the test
those that she loved
she had learned to detest

daddy i've got nothing left
my life is good
my love's a mess
daddy i've got nothing left
what can i do that's for the best?

daddy i've got nothing left
my life is good
my love's a mess
daddy i've got nothing left
what can i do that's for the best?

talk her down

you came waltzing in
where the love had been
and the boys all looked around
let me stay while you talk your baby down
i came waltzing in
where the light had been
and the girls all looked away
let them stare while we make our getaway

you came waltzing in
where the light had been
and the dark was all around
let me stay while they all fall to the ground

i was hiding from the weather
she was recently estranged
when she put me back together
didn't even know her name

you came waltzing in
where the life had been
and the death was all around
let them stare while they all fall to the ground

you came waltzing in
where the love had been
and the girls all looked away
let me stay while they make their getaway

i was hiding from the weather
she was recently estranged
when she put me back together
didn't even know her name

you came waltzing in
where your life had been
it was nowhere to be found
take me back to the place where we were bound

you came waltzing in
where the love had been
and the boys all looked around
let me stay while you talk your baby down

i was hiding from the weather
she was recently estranged
when she put me back together
didn't even know her name

love is here

if you could see the lover in me
and we could join our hands together
if you could see how good it could be
we'll sing these stupid songs forever

can you feel it?
love is here
it has never been so clear
you can't love what you have not
so hold on to what you've got

is judy really smiling for me?
i'd change my name in case she found me
trembling i can't believe
i've got to leave the girl behind me

can you feel it?
love is here
it has never been so clear
you can't love what you have not
so hold on to what you've got

if you could see the aching in me
i'd change my name in case you lost me
trembling down to my knees
i've got to leave the world behind me

can you feel it?
love is here
it has never been so clear
you can't love what you have not
so hold on to what you've got

good souls

feel
sick after every meal
i'd say
as i know
the life from your burning wheel
won't wane

sleep
i sleep every day
wipe the cobwebs away
i need to be loved
christ
i'm out of my mind
i need to be loved
i need to be loved

as i turn to you and i say
thank goodness for the good souls
that make life better
as i turn to you and i say
if it wasn't for the good souls
life would not matter

dive straight in on your girlfriend
making her feel like there's going to be a war
dive straight in at the deep end
making you feel like there's going to be a war

as i turn to you and i say
thank goodness for the good souls
that make life better
as i turn to you and i say
if it wasn't for the good souls
life would not matter

one good day of the week
and i'll be up again
one good day of the week
i'll be higher than the government

as i turn to you and i say
thank goodness for the good souls
that make life better
as i turn to you and i say
if you're messing with a good heart
you've got to take what's due

coming down

if you don't mind
could we not fight?
i see you're close woman
in the night
i'm sober
still alive

waste your days
on your own
getting drunk
getting stoned
i'm sober
still alone

must i always take a back seat?
must i always be your clown?
did you ever really love me?
were you always coming down?

see your face
see your eyes
shouldn't have left
shouldn't have lied
i'm sober
spirit's died

must i always take a back seat?
must i always be your clown?
did you ever really love me?
were you always coming down?

must i always take a back seat?
must i always be your clown?
did you ever really love me?
were you always coming down?

www.starsailor.net

starsailor are james walsh, james stelfox,
ben byrne & barry westhead

tie up my hands

Words and Music by James Walsh, James Stelfox, Barry Westhead and Benjamin Byrne

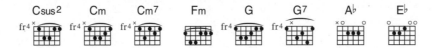

Tune all Gtrs. down one half-step

5

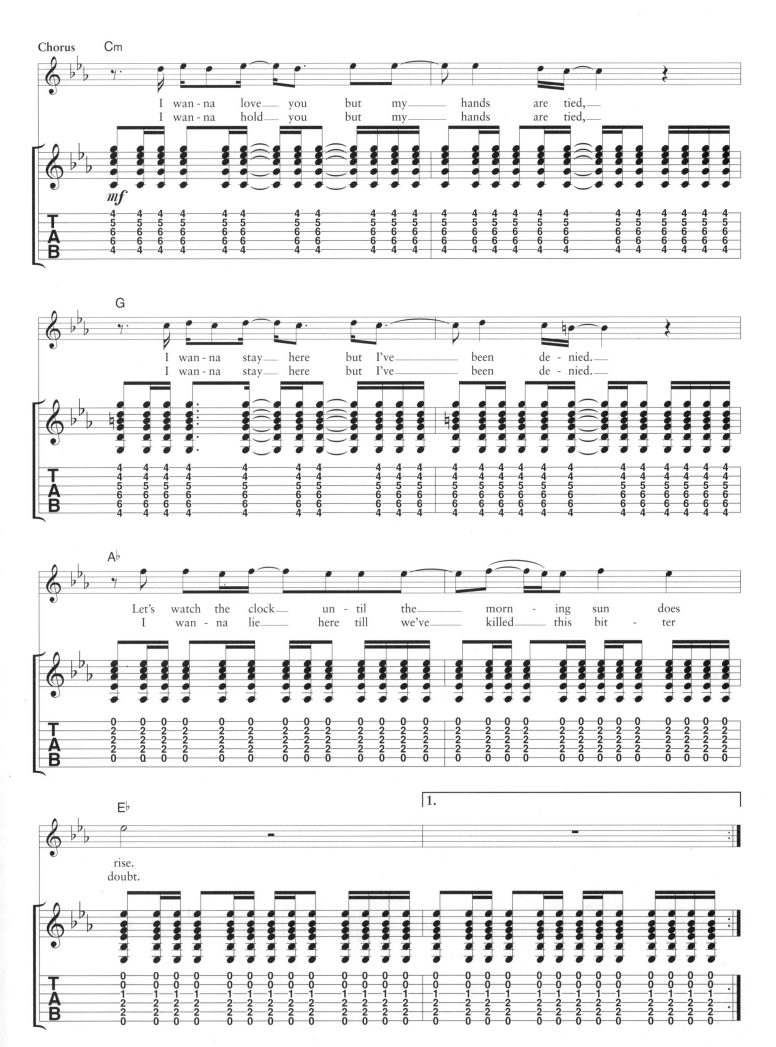

Chorus Cm

I wan-na love___ you but my___ hands are tied,___
I wan-na hold___ you but my___ hands are tied,___

mf

G

I wan-na stay___ here but I've___ been de-nied.___
I wan-na stay___ here but I've___ been de-nied.___

A♭

Let's watch the clock___ un-til the___ morn-ing sun does
I wan-na lie___ here till we've___ killed___ this bit-ter

1.

E♭

rise.
doubt.

7

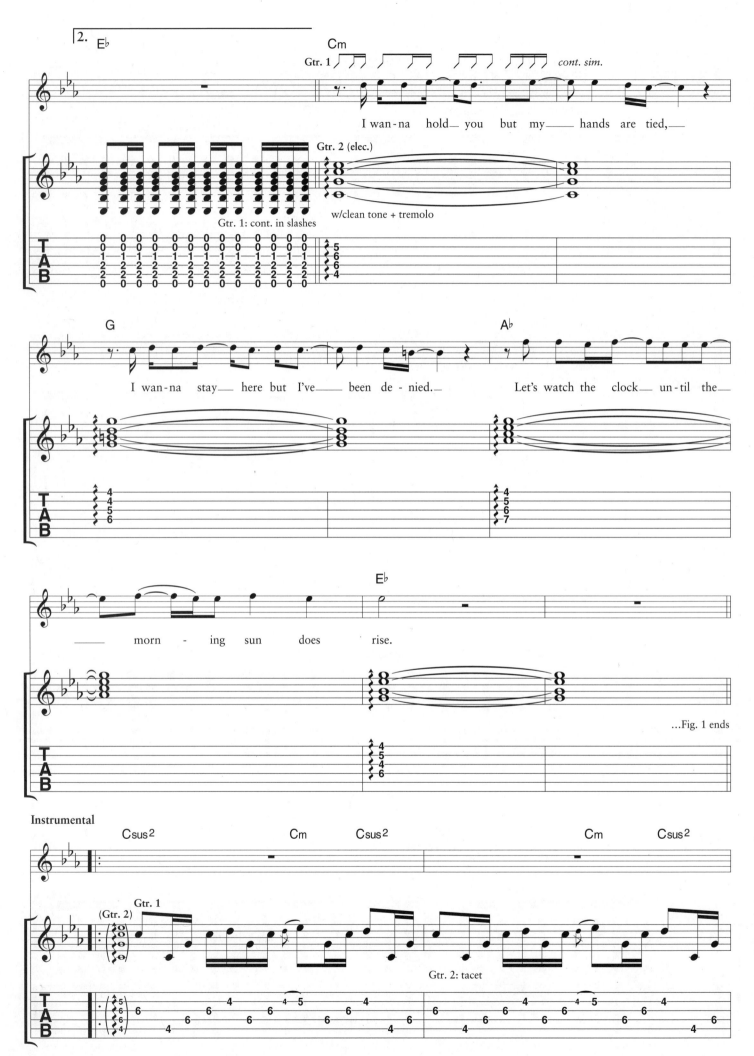

Lyrics:

I wan-na hold— you but my— hands are tied,—

I wan-na stay— here but I've— been de-nied.—

Let's watch the clock— un-til the—

—— morn-ing sun does rise.

...Fig. 1 ends

Instrumental

Chorus

1. I wan-na hold— you but my——— hands are tied,—
2. I wan-na hold— you but my——— hands are tied,—
(3° + 4° vocal ad lib.)

Gtr. 1 + Gtr. 3 (elec.)

Gtr. 3: w/slight crunch
Gtr. 2: w/Fig. 1

9

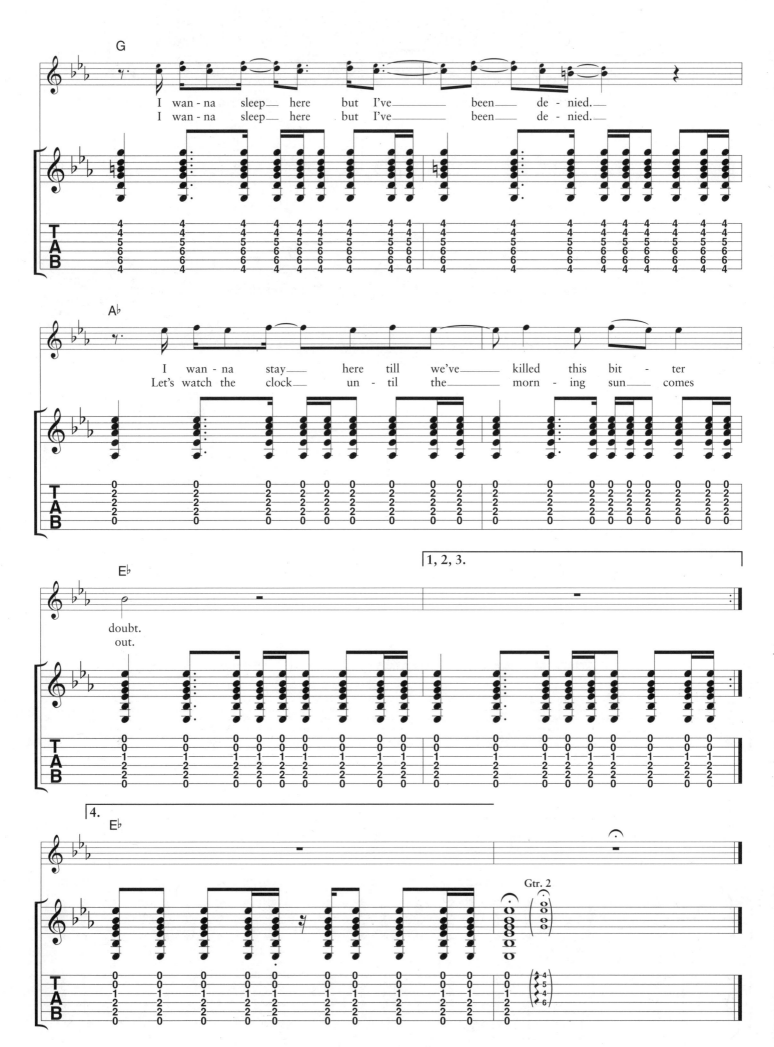

10

poor misguided fool

Words and Music by James Walsh, James Stelfox, Barry Westhead and Benjamin Byrne

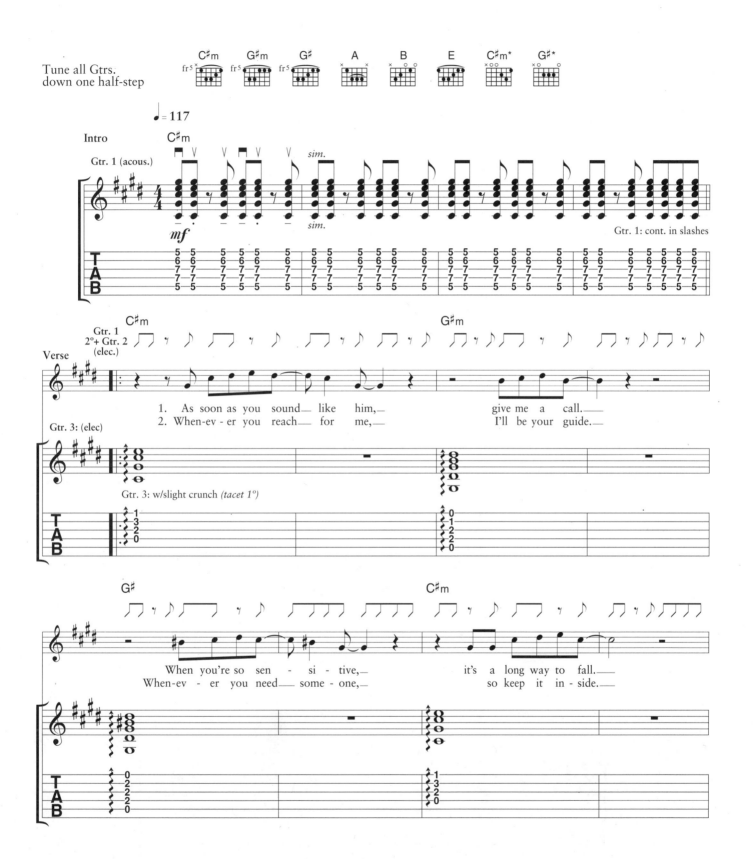

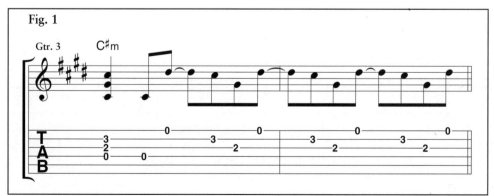

alcoholic

Words and Music by James Walsh, James Stelfox, Barry Westhead and Benjamin Byrne

I was look-ing for an-oth-er you,— when I looked round you were gone.—

Chorus

Stay by my— side and the— pipe - dream is yours— now.

Stay by my— side and the {sin - ger / cy - nics} won't get— in our— way.

1° Gtr. 1: w/Fig. 1

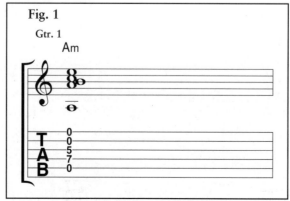

Fig. 1

Gtr. 1

Am

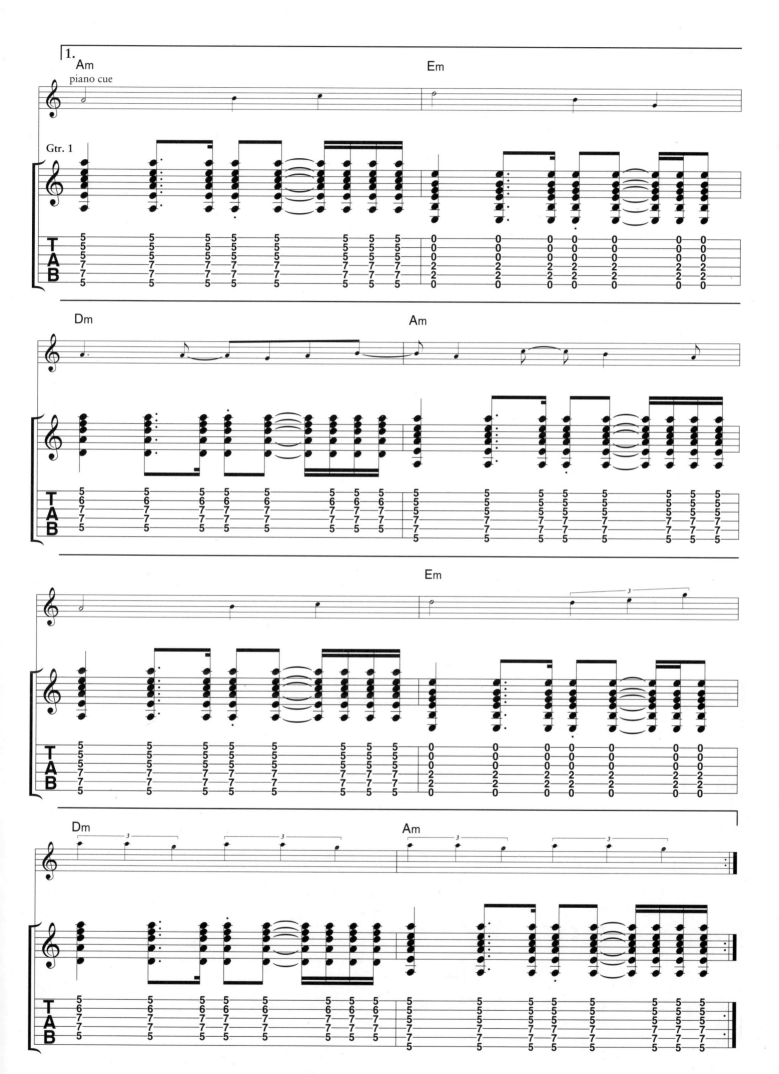

lullaby

Words and Music by James Walsh, James Stelfox, Barry Westhead and Benjamin Byrne

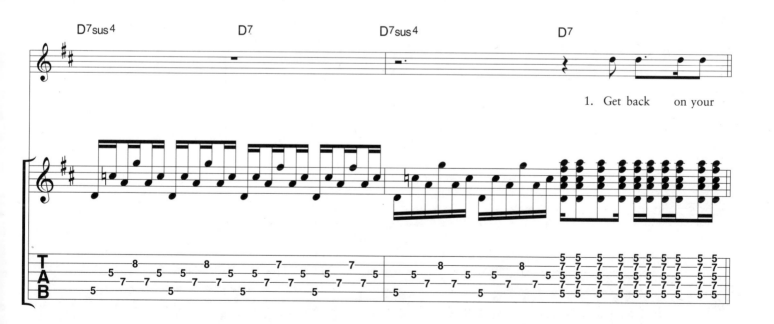

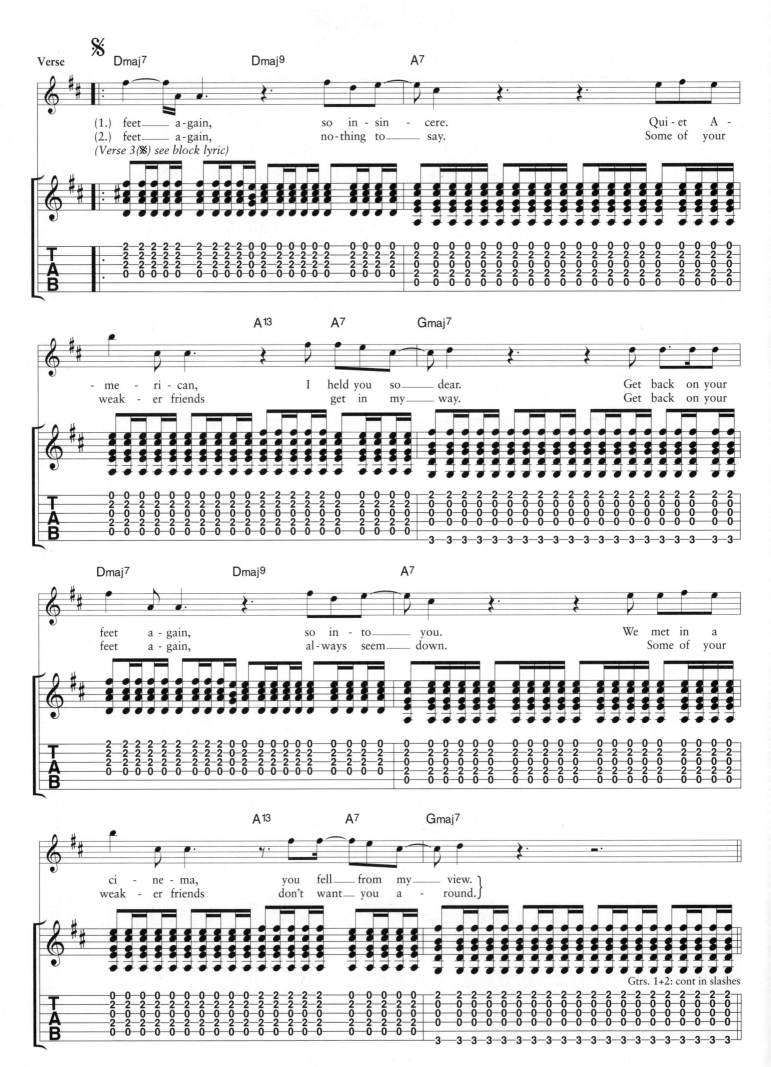

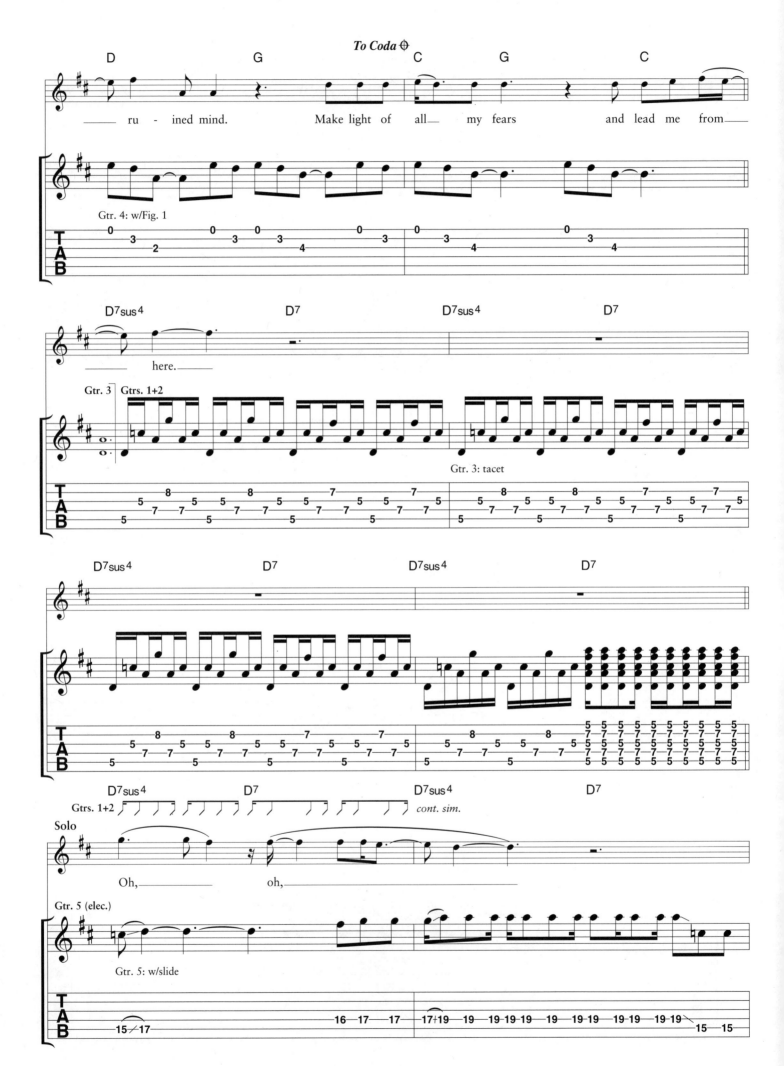

Verse 3:
Get back on your feet again
So insincere
Quiet American, I held you so dear
Get back on your feet again
Nothing to say
We met in a cinema
You got in my way.

Lullaby *etc.*

way to fall

Words and Music by James Walsh, James Stelfox, Barry Westhead and Benjamin Byrne

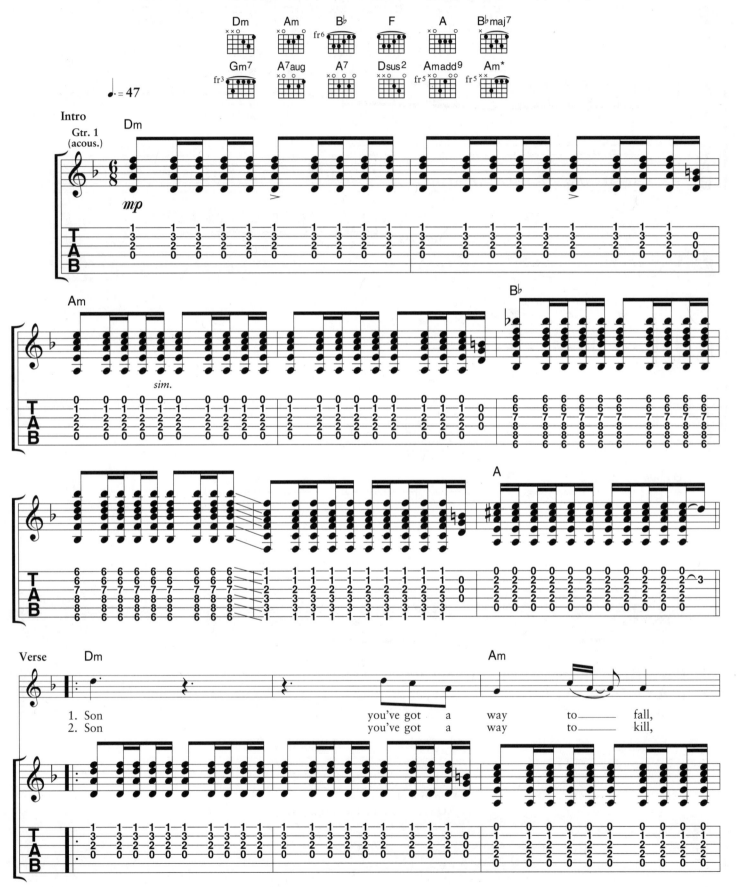

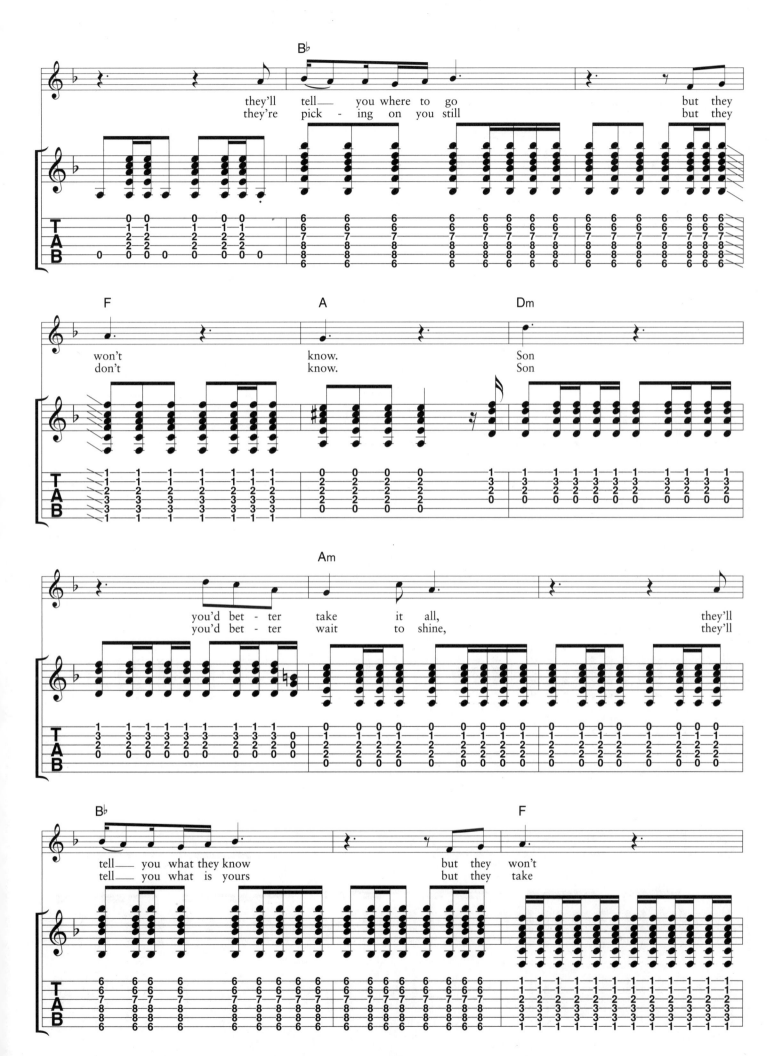

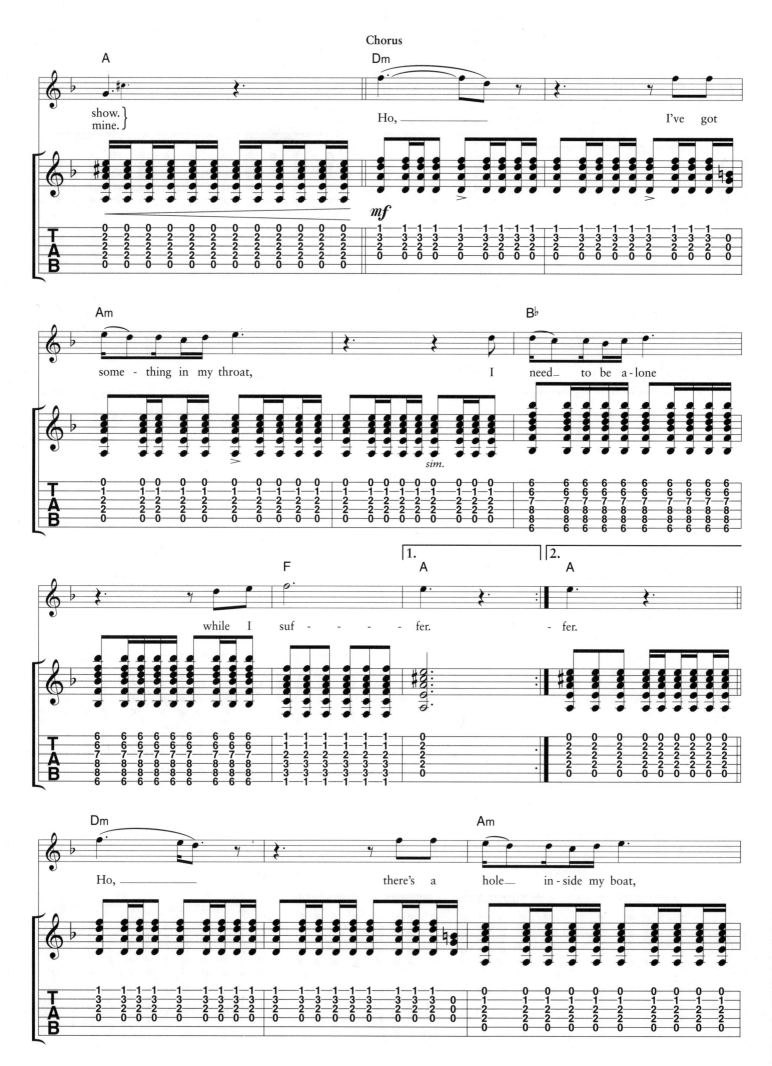

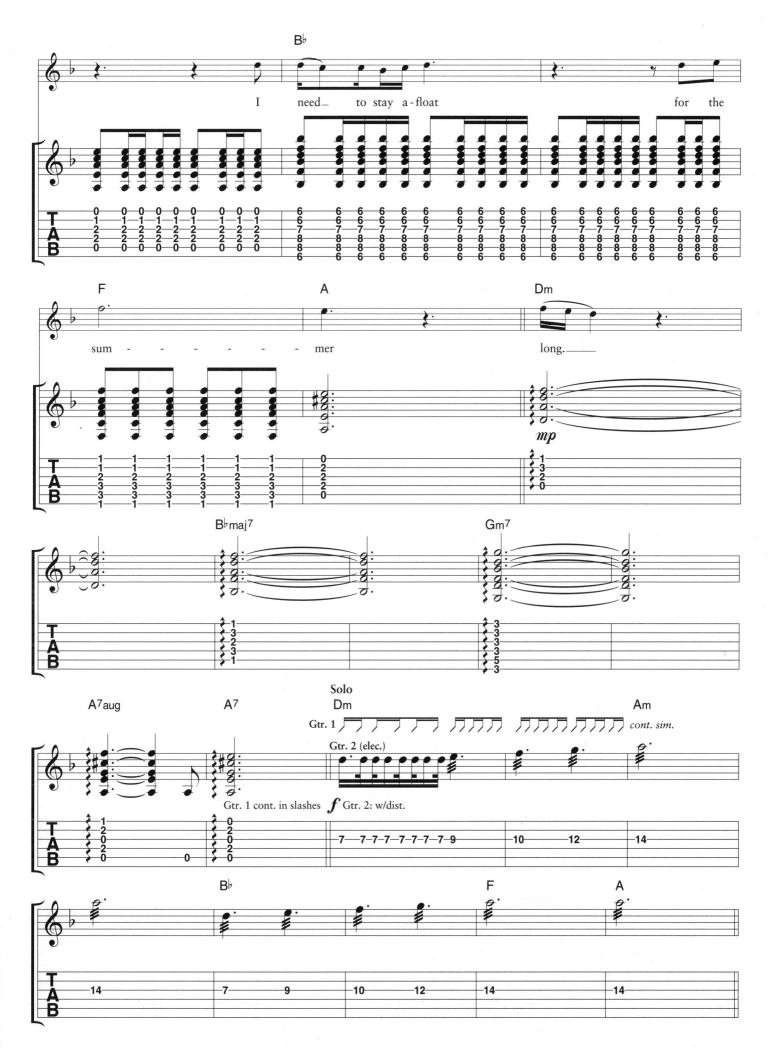

fever

Words and Music by James Walsh, James Stelfox, Barry Westhead and Benjamin Byrne

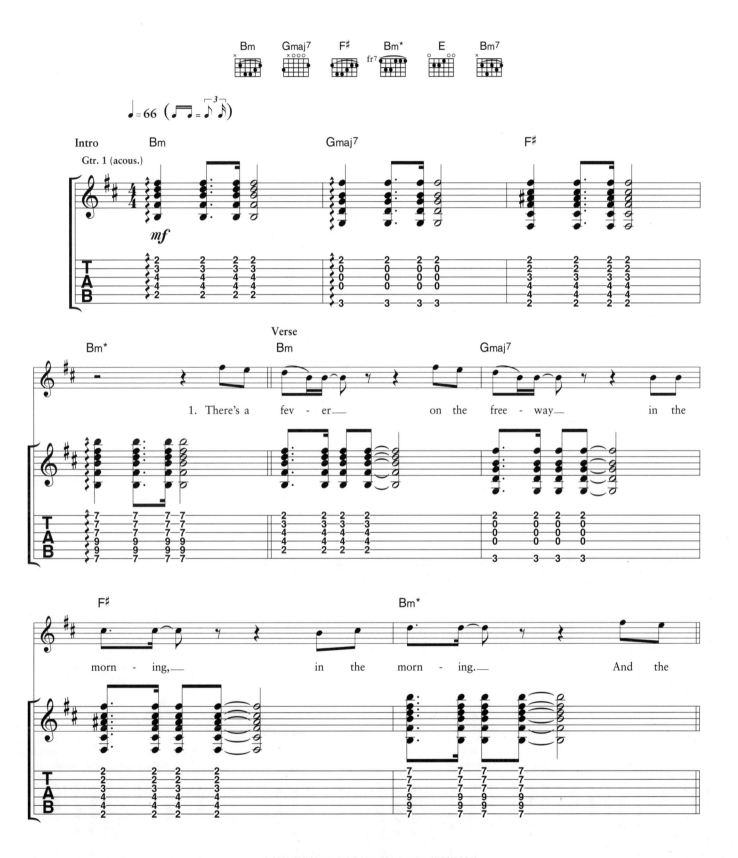

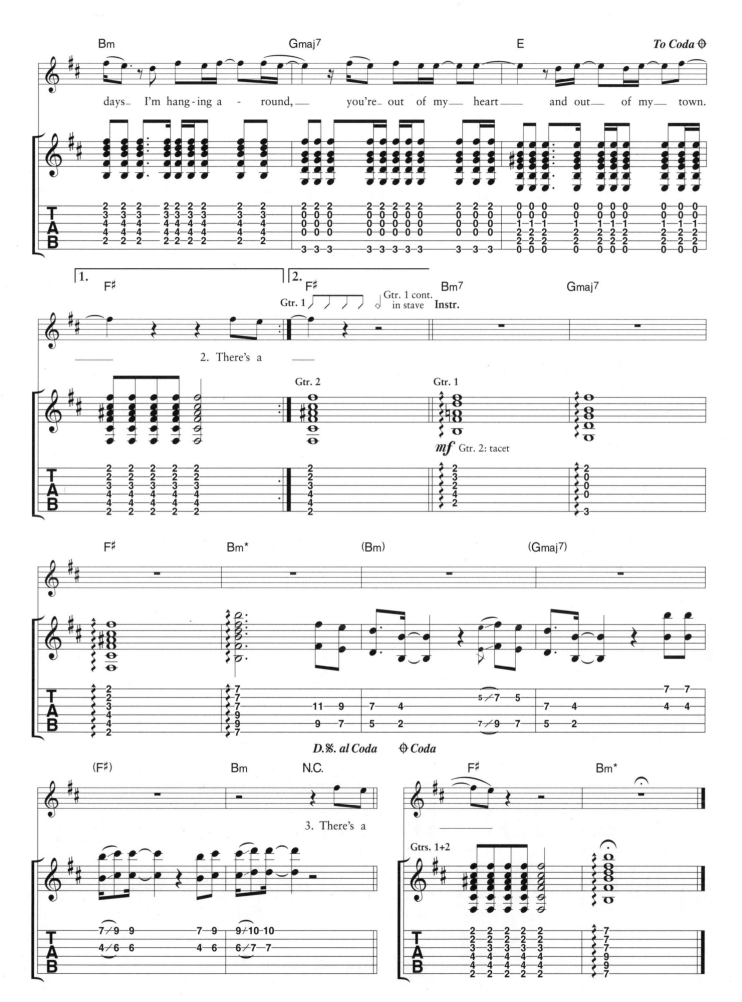

she just wept

Words and Music by James Walsh, James Stelfox, Barry Westhead and Benjamin Byrne

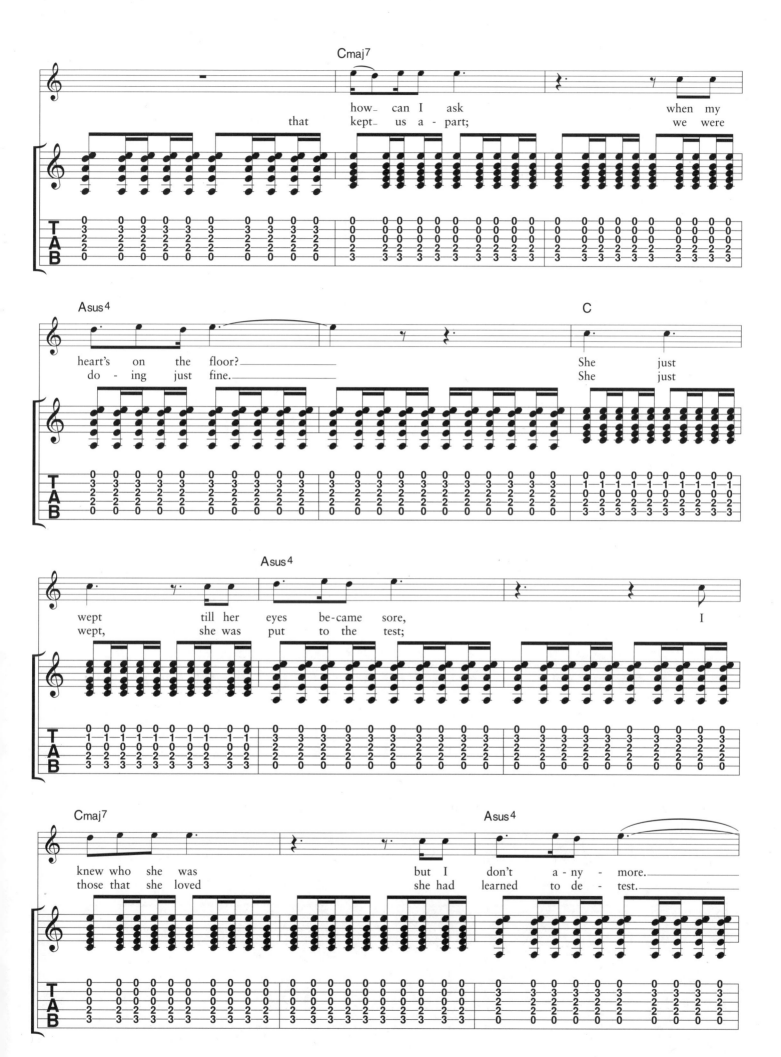

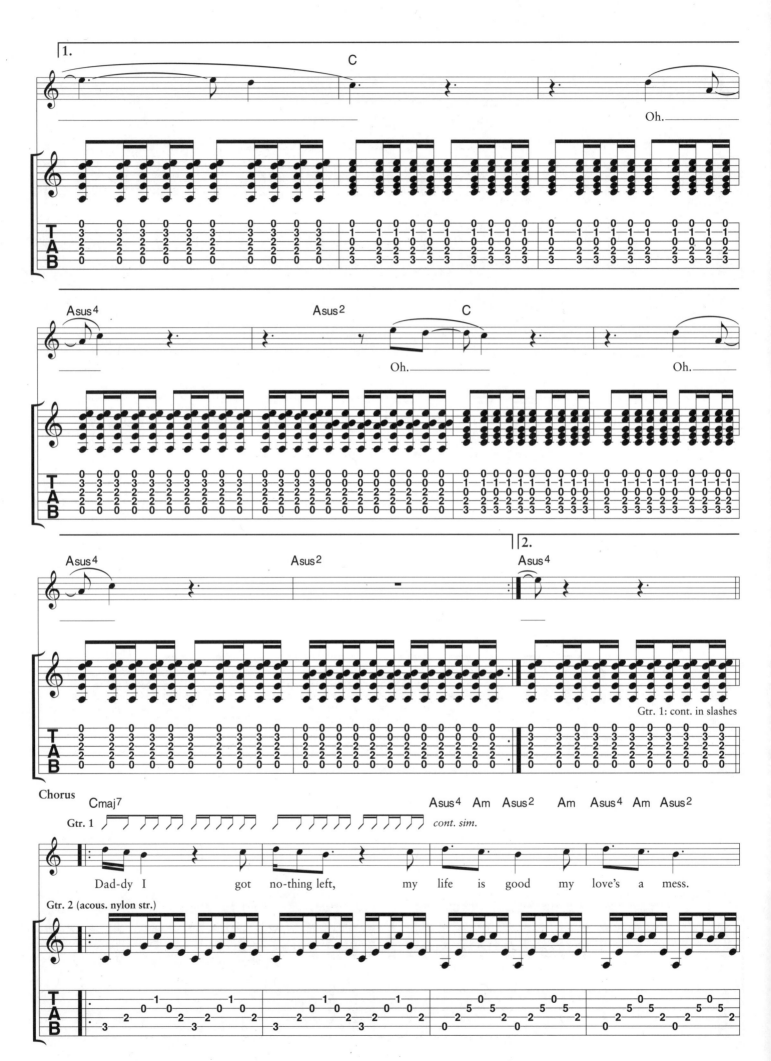

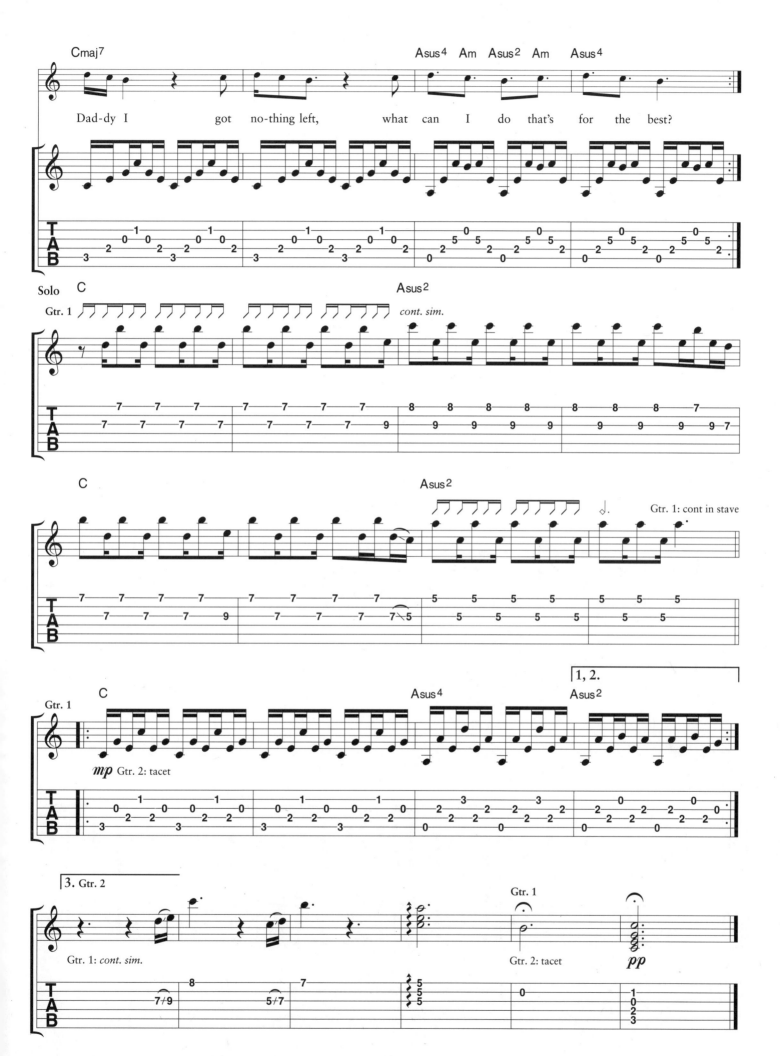

talk her down

Words and Music by James Walsh, James Stelfox, Barry Westhead and Benjamin Byrne

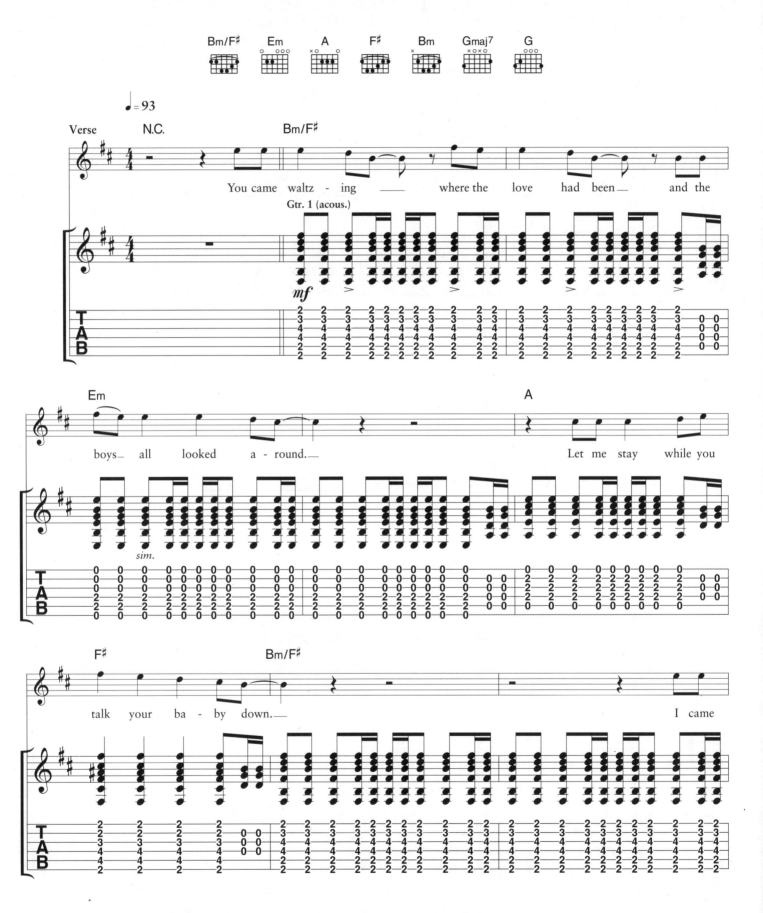

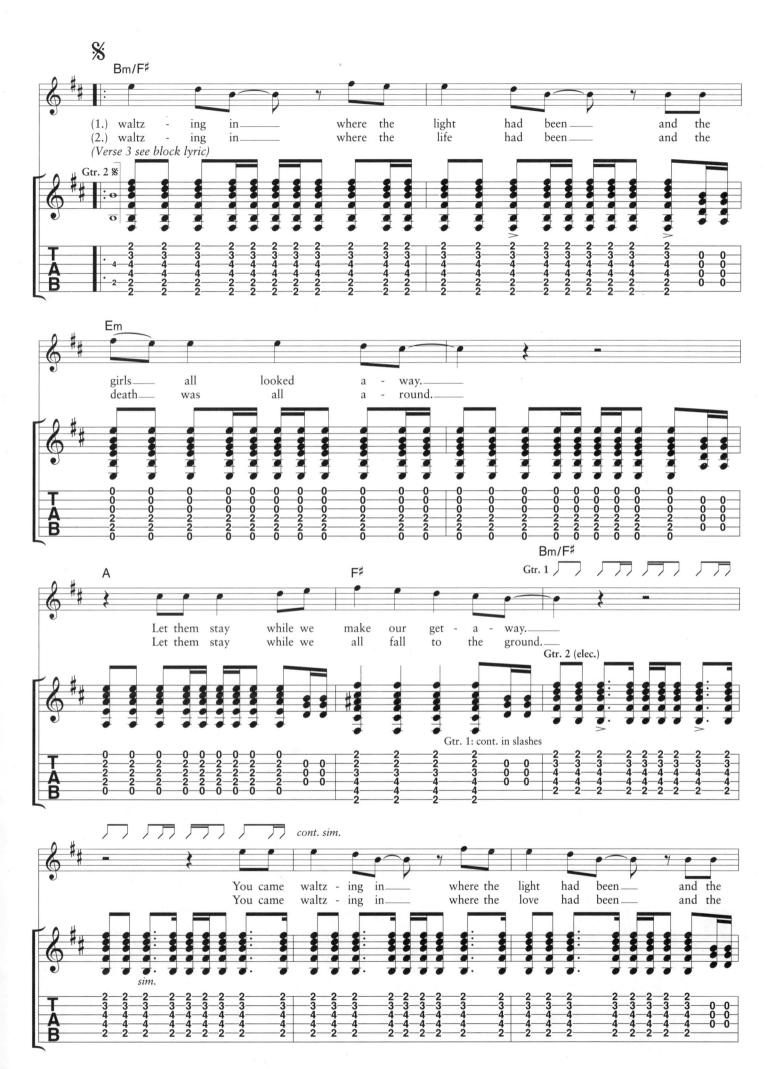

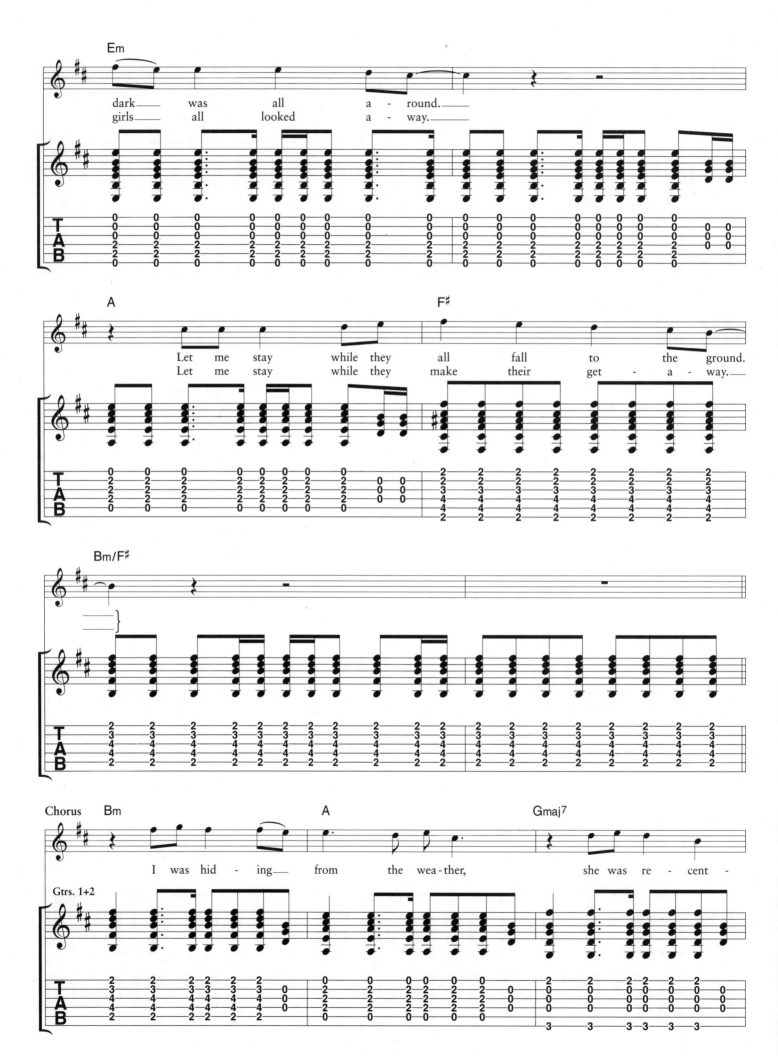

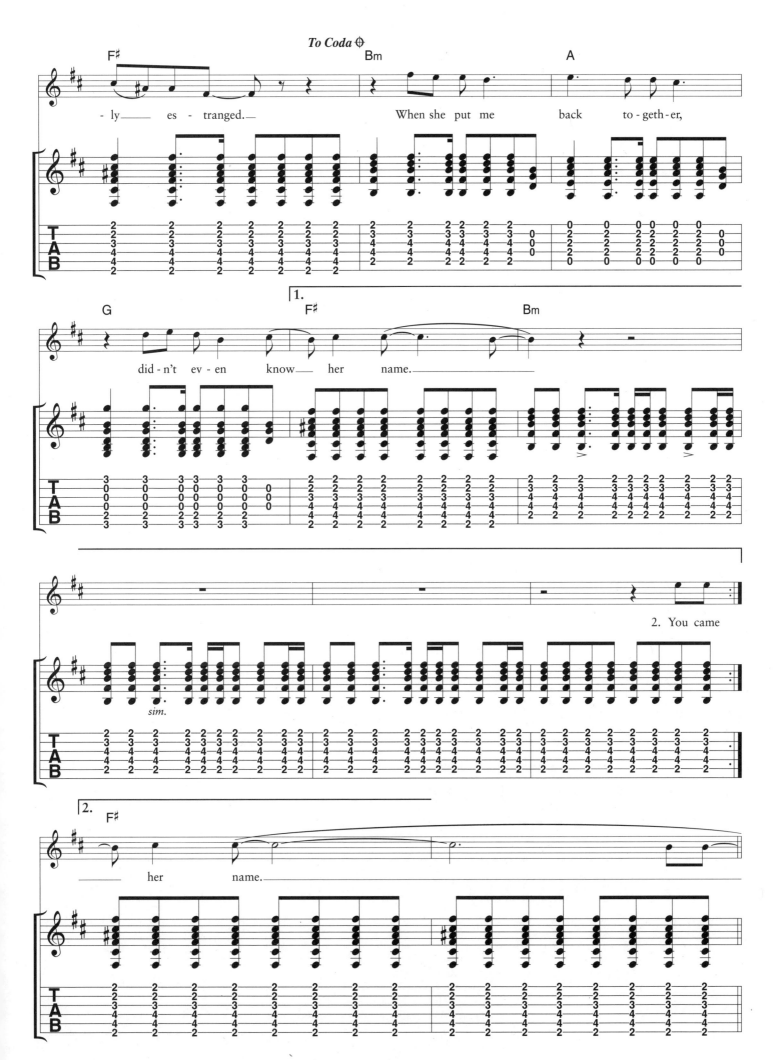

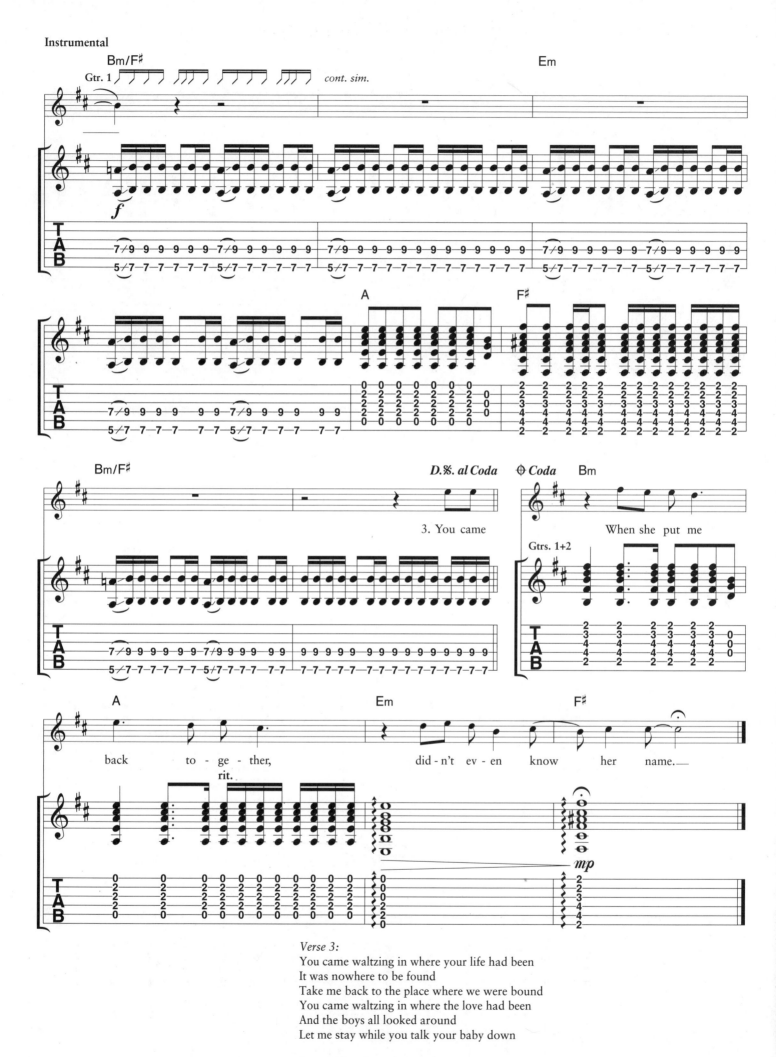

Verse 3:
You came waltzing in where your life had been
It was nowhere to be found
Take me back to the place where we were bound
You came waltzing in where the love had been
And the boys all looked around
Let me stay while you talk your baby down

I was hiding from the weather *etc.*

love is here

Words and Music by James Walsh, James Stelfox, Barry Westhead and Benjamin Byrne

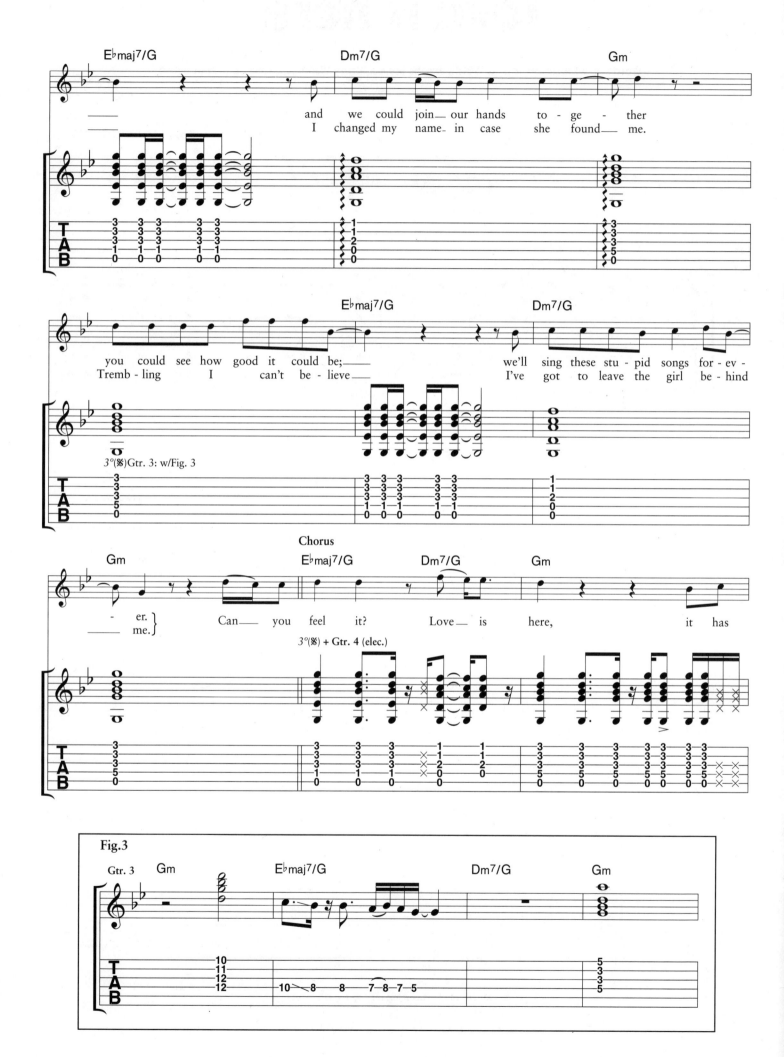

Gtr. 1: w/Fig. 2 (x4)

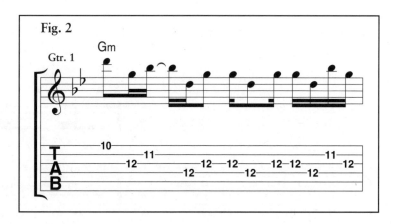

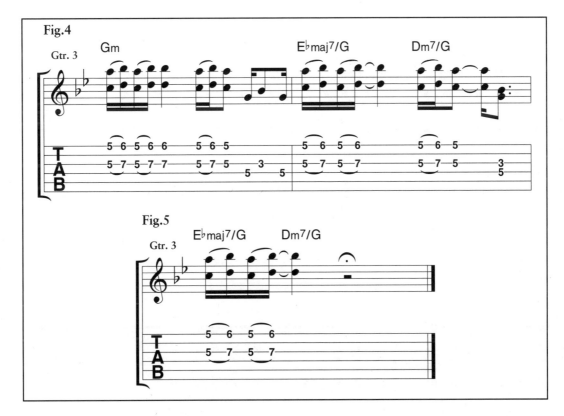

Verse 3:
If you could see the aching in me
I'd change my name in case you lost me
Trembling down to my knees
I've got to leave the world behind me.

Can you feel it *etc.*

good souls

Words and Music by James Walsh, James Stelfox, Barry Westhead and Benjamin Byrne

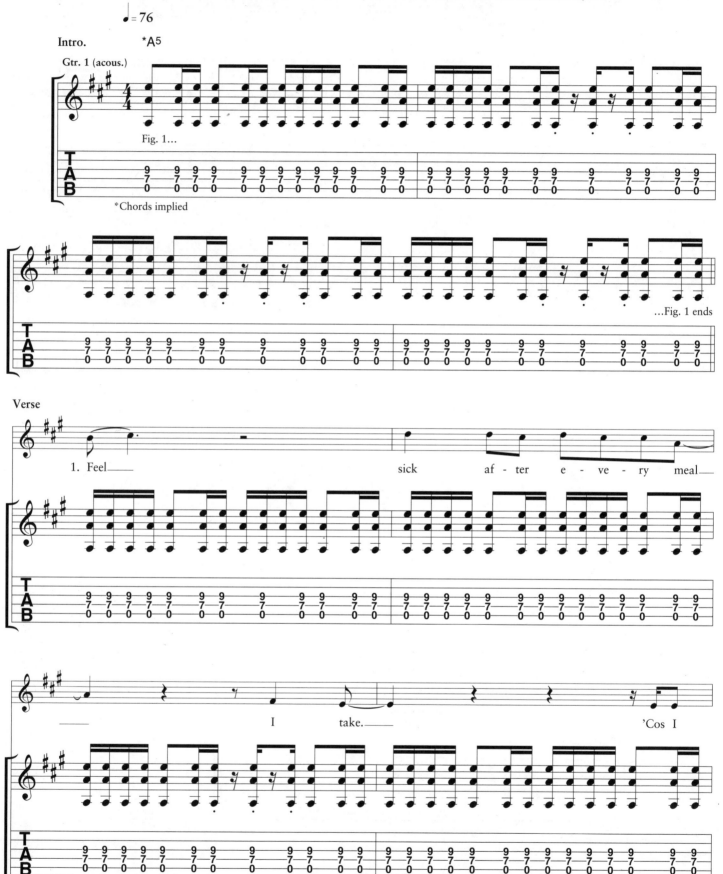

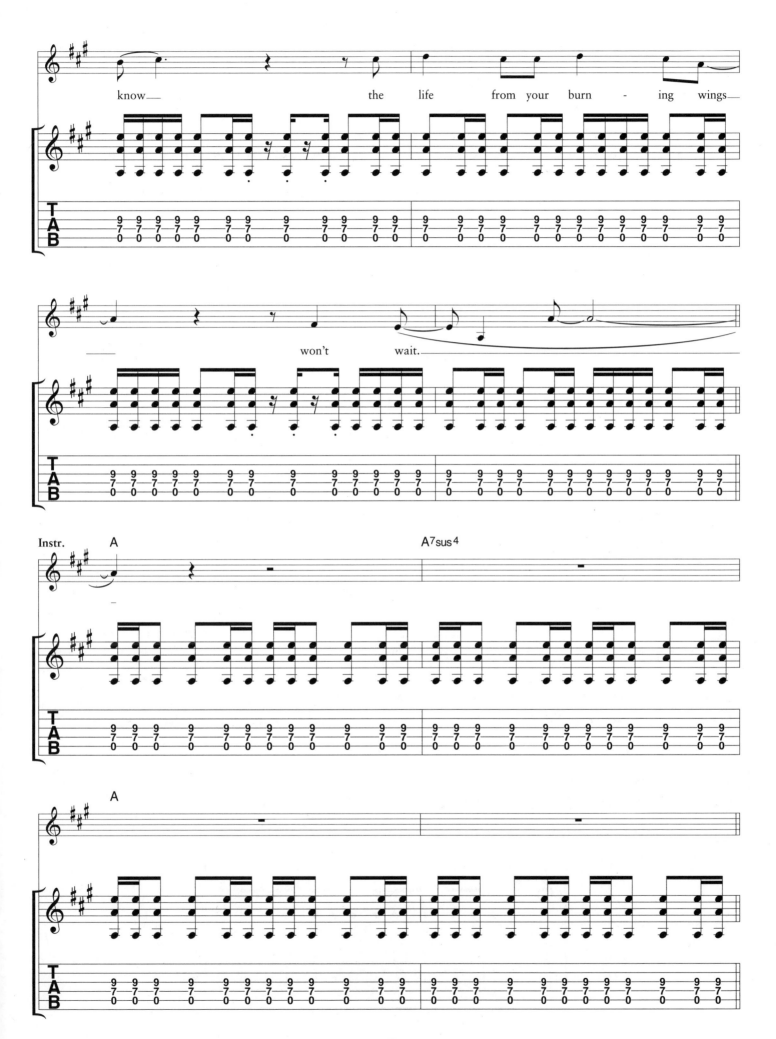

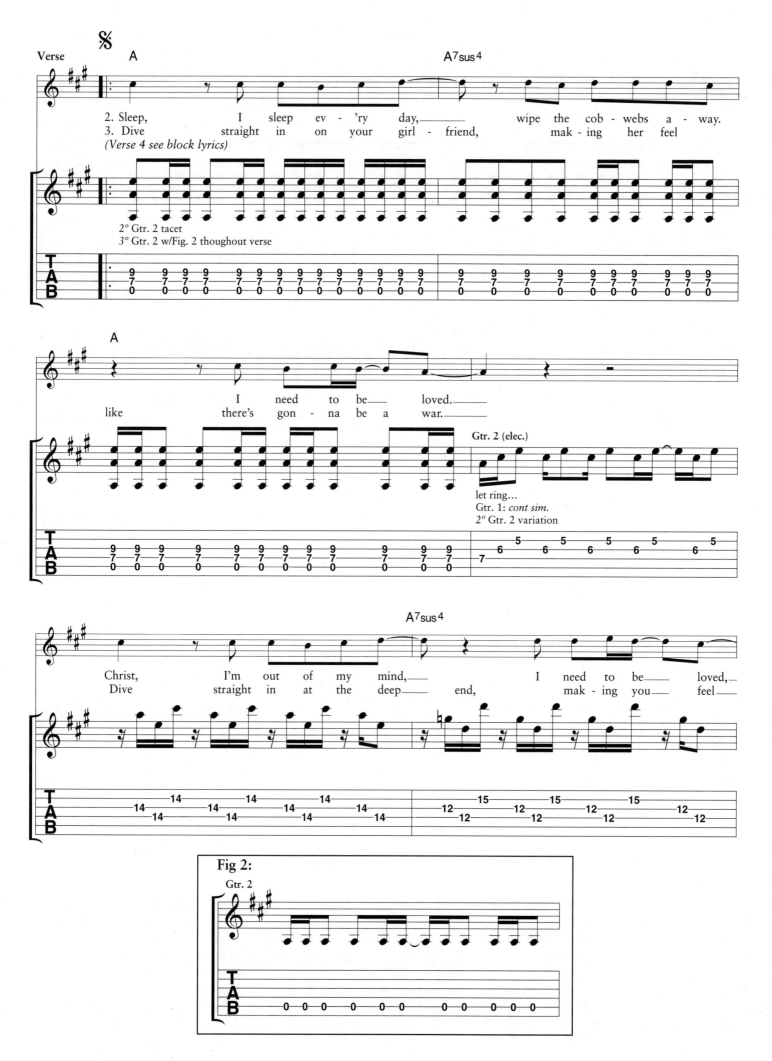

As I turn to you and I say, thank good-ness for the good souls, that make life bet-ter.

As I turn to you and I say, if it was-n't for the good souls, life would not mat-ter.

2.
Instr.
A
A7sus4
A
D.%. al Coda
Gtr. 2: tremolo pedal off
Gtr. 1: w/Fig. 1
Gtr. 3: w/Fig. 3
Coda
A
Amaj7
D
F
G
Gtr. 1
cont. sim.
As I turn to you and I say, you're mess-ing with a good heart, you've got - ta take what's due.
Gtr. 2
Gtr. 2 w/tremolo pedal
A
A7sus4
A
A7sus4
Gtr. 3: w/Fig. 3
Fig 3:
Gtr. 2

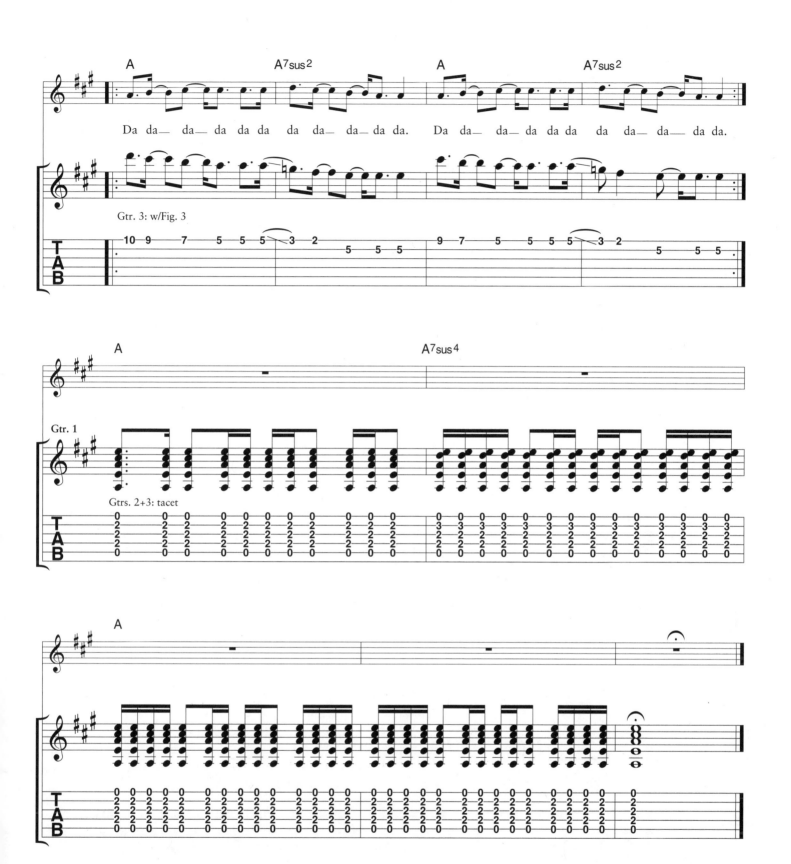

Da da— da— da da da   da da— da— da da.   Da da— da— da da da   da da— da— da da.

Gtr. 3: w/Fig. 3

Gtr. 1

Gtrs. 2+3: tacet

Verse 4:
One good day of the week
And I'll be up again.
One good day of the week
I'll be higher than the government.

coming down

Words and Music by James Walsh, James Stelfox, Barry Westhead and Benjamin Byrne

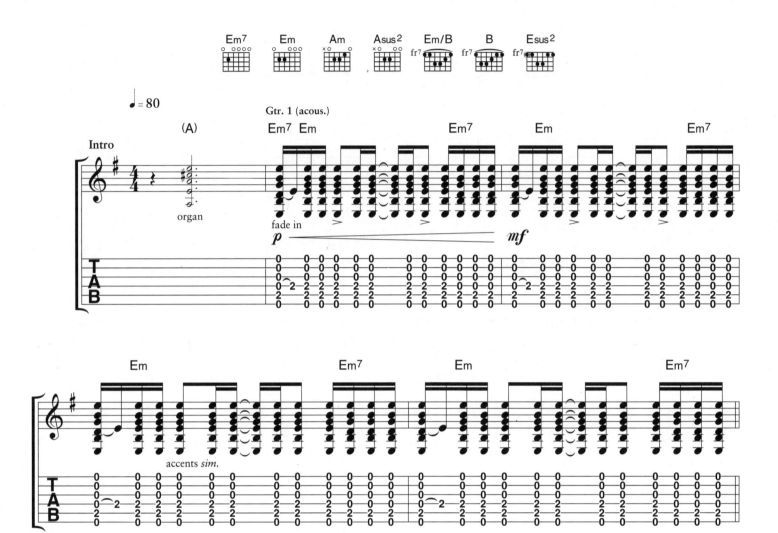

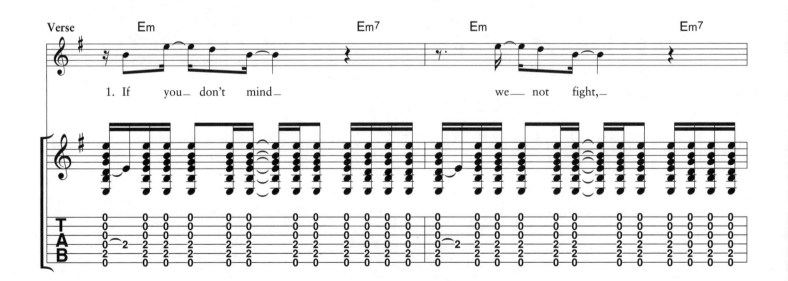

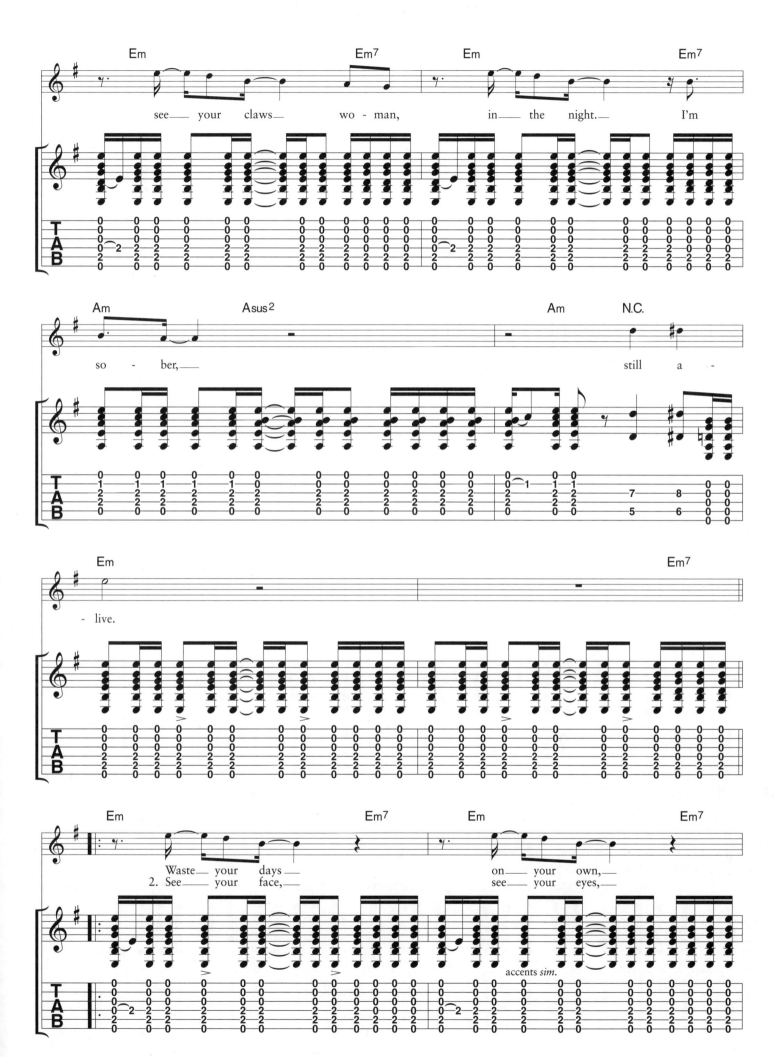

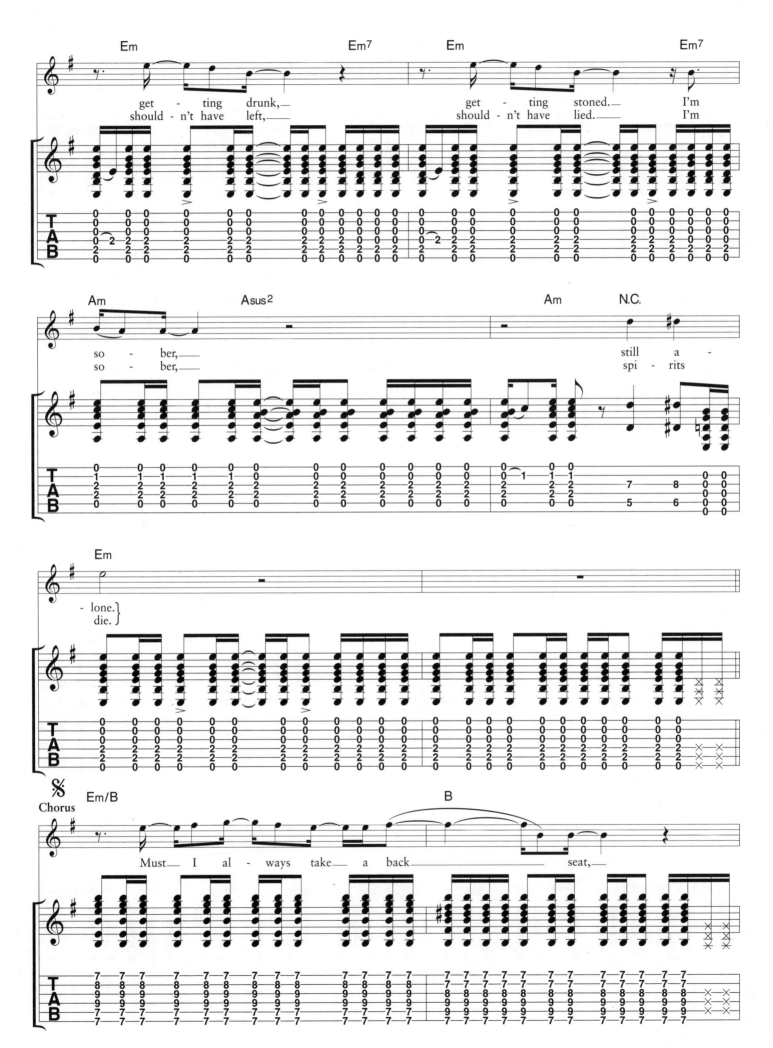

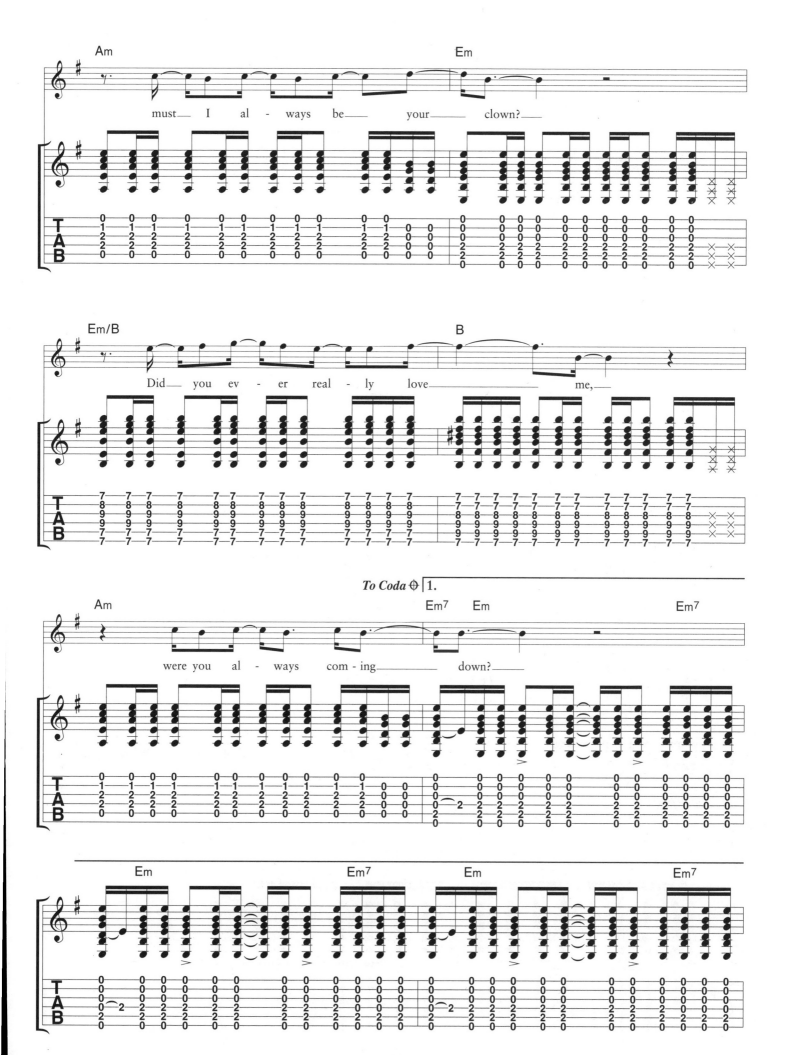

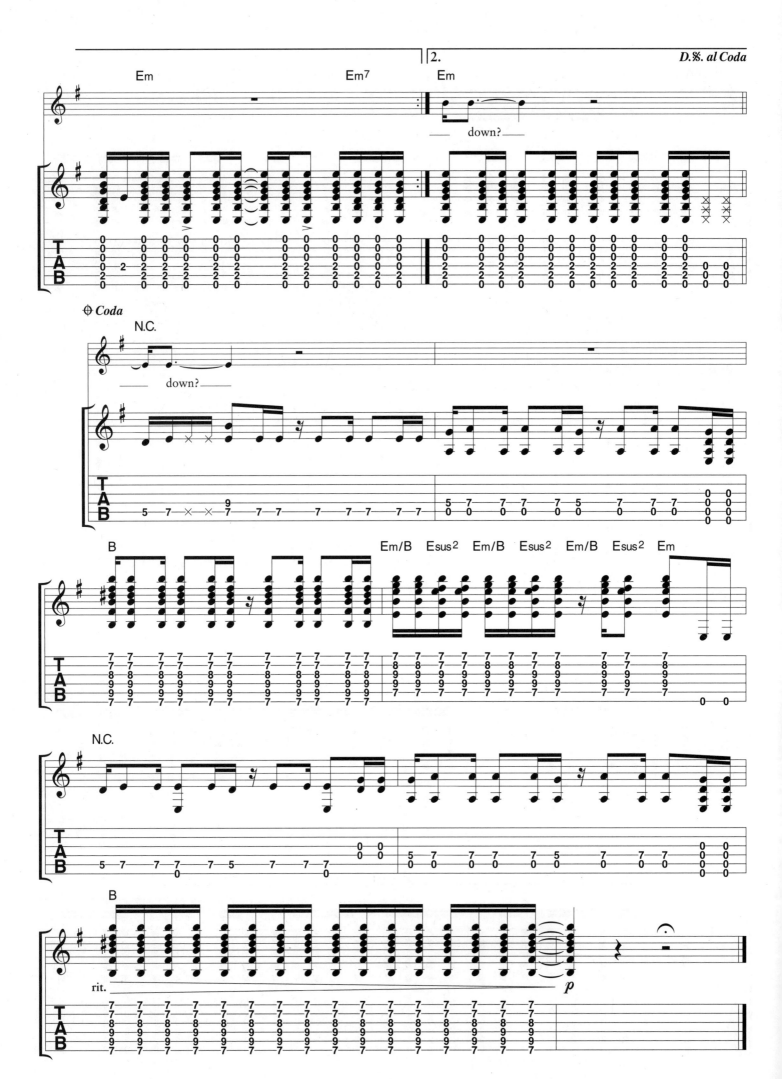